Ages 3-4

Leap Ahead Workbook
English
Home learning made fun

Leap Ahead

Cat

Frog

Dog

Preschool English

igloobooks

This is Me!

Draw a picture of yourself:

Write your name:

PARENT TIP: Your child might find it difficult to hold a pencil at this age. However, they will love trying to write their own name, even if it is simply to make letter-like marks.
It's a great way to start writing!

Sounds All Around

Look at each picture. What sound does it make?
Can you make the sound LOUDLY and quietly?

Pet Pairs

Look carefully at the shapes to see which ones match. Draw a line between each pair.

(a)

(1)

(b)

(2)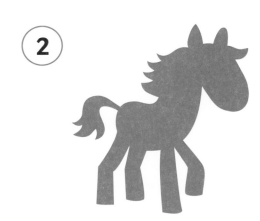

(c)

(3)

(d)

(4)

Answers on page 32

Animal Patterns

Look carefully at each row of animal pairs and circle the odd one out.

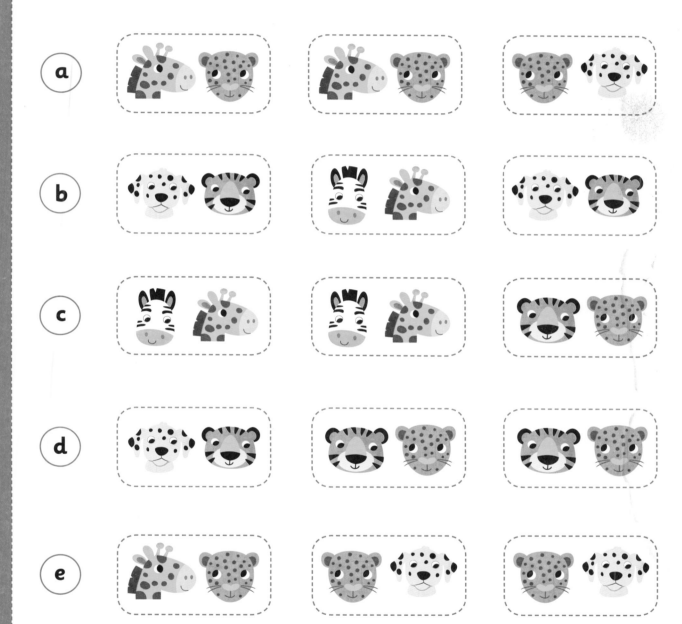

Answers on page 32

PARENT TIP: Matching outlines and patterns is a great way to prepare a child for identifying letter shapes. Encourage them to focus on the similarities and details of patterns and shapes.

It's Time to Rhyme!

Look at the pictures in each row and say the words. Then, find the correct items on your sticker sheet whose names rhyme with each word in that row.

1. frog   log

2. cat   bat

3. coat   goat

PARENT TIP: Being able to hear when words rhyme is one of the first steps in learning to read and spell. Children need to separate the words they say into different sounds, for example, 'p-i-g'. This is called sound-talking. Later, they will learn to link sounds with letters.

④ wig   dig

⑤   sing   sting

⑥ ham   lamb

⑦ claw   paw

7

Over the Moon

Follow the arrows to draw around these planets. Can you find some spaceship stickers on your sticker sheet to land on them?

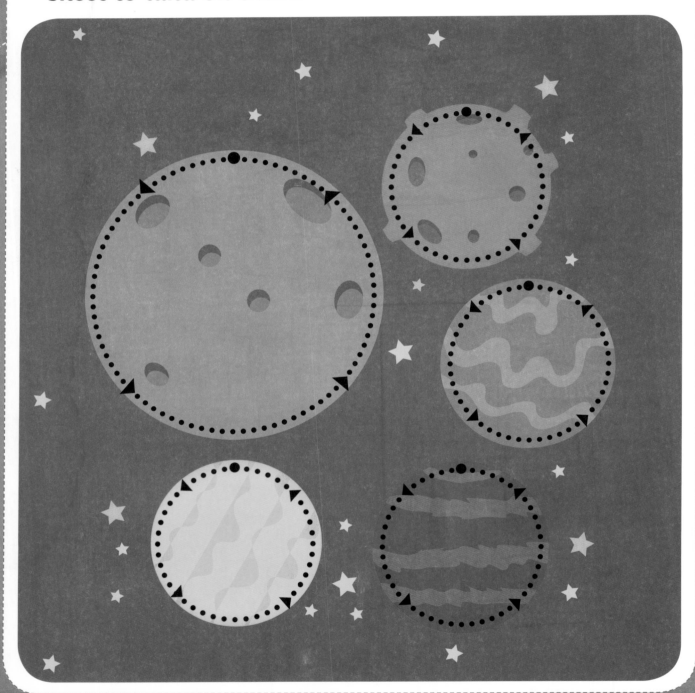

PARENT TIP: It takes a while for children to learn to write letters properly, but making big patterns and shapes is a good way to start.

Space Message

Ace the Alien has been learning about letters. Help him by following the arrows to make these letter shapes.

PARENT TIP: All these letters are made using round shapes, like the planets on the opposite page.

9

Odd Rhyme Out

Look at the pictures in each row and say the words out loud. Colour the two words that rhyme in blue. Colour the word that doesn't rhyme in red.

hand   **sand**   **sheep**

1

2

PARENT TIP: Your child might need to practise before they can hear words which rhyme. Help them to hear rhyming sounds by saying, "I've got a spoon. What can you see that sounds like spoon?"

Farmer Fred's Fence

Follow the arrows and finish the fence to help Farmer Fred. Then, add some sheep stickers from your sticker sheet.

Now, follow the arrows to practise writing these letters.

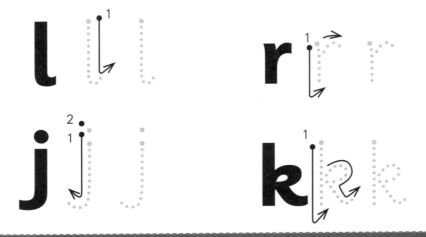

'a' and 's' Words

Colour the items that start with 'a' in red.
Colour the items that with 's' in blue.
Circle the items that don't start with either letter.

sunglasses

arrow

PARENT TIP: Help your child to say the sound made by each letter, e.g.
'a' for 'apple', 's' for 'sock'. Then, sound-talk the names of each item.

13

Ocean I Spy

Play I Spy with this ocean scene and see how many items you can spot. For example, "I spy with my little eye, something beginning with... d."

PARENT TIP: When you play 'I Spy', take care how you say the first sound in each word ('t' not 'tuh', for example). Take it in turns to choose a letter and guess the answer. Don't worry if your child says the wrong answer. Give them lots of praise for trying.

Add some sea stickers of your own

All at Sea

It's a nice day out at sea. Follow the arrows to draw some waves around the fishing boat, then add some seagull stickers in the sky.

Now, follow the arrows to practise writing these letters.

't' and 'p' Words

Colour the items that start with 't' in red.
Colour the items that start with 'p' in blue.
Circle the items that don't start with either letter.

pen

t

tent

p

10

Same Sound Stickers

Look at the pictures and say the word out loud. Find a sticker to match the same beginning sound as the other two words in that row.

1. **s**ock   **s**ack   sand

2. tap   ten

3. nest   neck

4. bed   bag

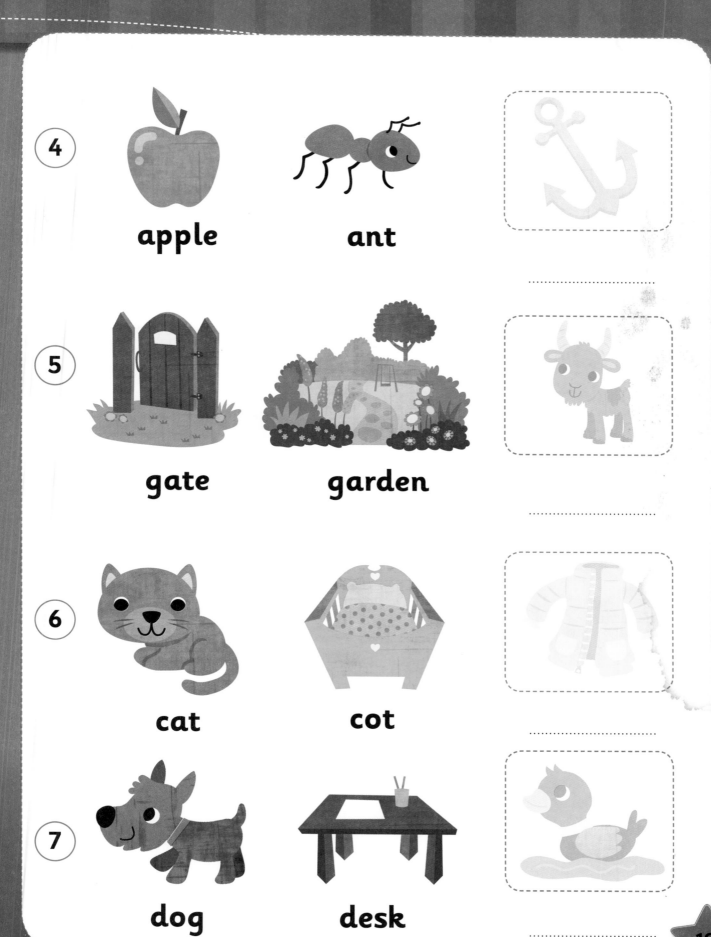

(4) apple ant

(5) gate garden

(6) cat cot

(7) dog desk

Lily Pad Letters

Look at these happy frogs. Follow the arrows to draw the shape they make as they hop from one lily pad to the next.

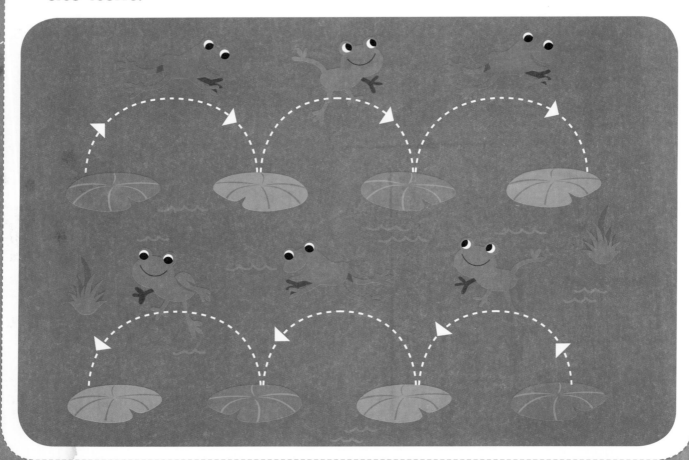

Now, follow the arrows to practise writing these letters.

'n' and 'm' Words

Colour the items that start with 'n' in red.
Colour the items that starts with 'm' in blue.
Circle the items that don't start with either letter.

net

man

Odd Toy Out

These toys have letters on them, but the odd letters out keep getting in the way!
Circle the odd letter out in each row.

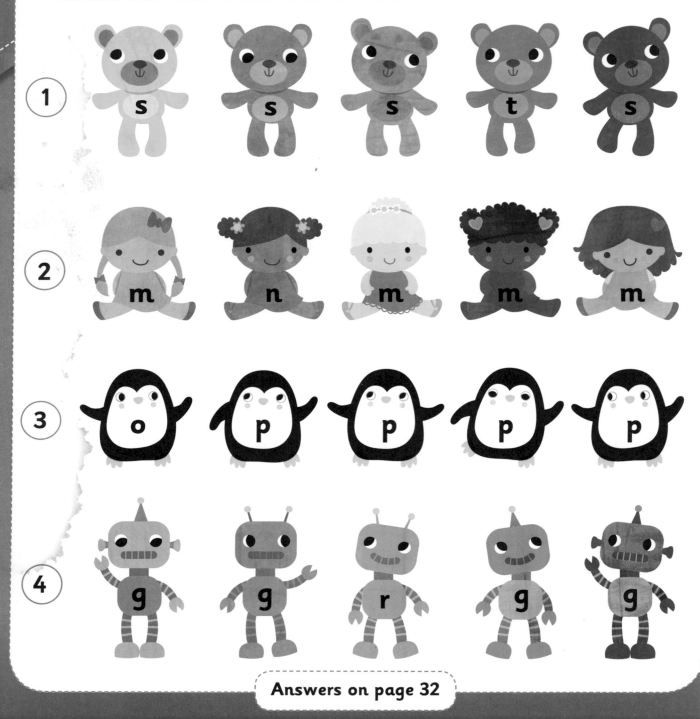

1. s s s t s

2. m n m m m

3. o p p p p

4. g g r g g

Answers on page 32

PARENT TIP: Being able to recognise letters quickly is essential when your child starts to read. Encourage them to focus on the little differences between letters.

Silly Sentences

Read the beginning of each silly sentence out loud.
What silly word will you put at the end?
Use the pictures to help.

 **Simon Sailor's sack is full of** ....

snails   **sand**   **slugs**

 **Wispy Witch wishes for a** ....

wand   **wasp**   **walrus**

 Millie Mouse makes a mess with ....

mud   **mittens**   **moles**

 **Billie Baker bakes** ....

biscuits   **bugs**   **beds**

PARENT TIP: You and your child can have fun making up your own sentences together. It's a great way to pass the time and encourage children to think creatively.

23

Zigzag Robots

Sammy Science has almost finished his robots. Help him to complete them by following the zigzag lines.

Now, follow the arrows to practise writing these letters.

'd' and 'g' Words

Colour the items that start with 'd' in red.
Colour the items that start with 'g' in blue.
Circle the items that don't start with either letter.

garden

d

g

dog

Rhyming I Spy

Look at the park scene and use these pictures to play Rhyming I Spy. For example, "I spy with my little eye, something that rhymes with... balloon."

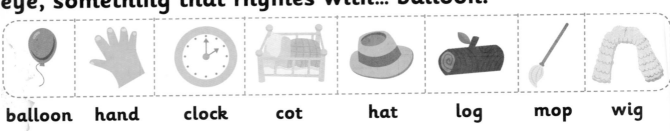

balloon   hand   clock   cot   hat   log   mop   wig

What's the Picture?

There's a shape hidden in the grid below. Colour the 'c' squares red and the 'k' squares yellow to find out what it is.

k	c	c	c	k	c	c	c	k
c	c	c	c	c	c	c	c	c
k	c	c	c	c	c	c	c	k
k	k	c	c	c	c	c	k	k
k	k	k	c	c	c	k	k	k
k	k	k	k	c	k	k	k	k
k	k	k	k	k	k	k	k	k

Answers on page 32

Aladdin's Magic Lamp

How many things in the cave can you find beginning with each of these sounds?

b	h	f	r

Hidden in the cave is Aladdin's magic lamp. When you find it, place the genie sticker from your sticker sheet by the lamp.

Me and My Sounds

What letter does your name start with?

....

Draw a picture of something that starts with the same sound as your name:

Draw a picture of you and your best friend:

What letter does your best friend's name start with?

Answers

Page 4: Pet Pairs

a – 3, b – 4, c – 2, d – 1

Page 5: Animal Patterns

a

b

c

d

e

Page 22: Odd Toy Out

1   2   3   4

Page 28: What's the Picture?

A heart.

page 6-7

page 8

page 12

page 14

page 16

page 18-19

page 29